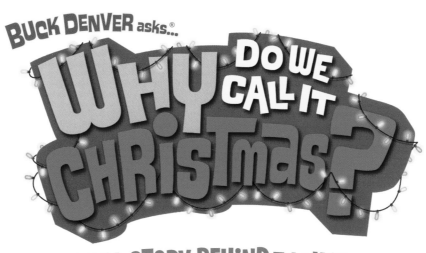

BUCK DENVER asks...
WHY DO WE CALL IT CHRISTMAS?

THE REAL STORY BEHIND THE HOLIDAY

Written by Phil Vischer

Illustrated by Jeremiah Alcorn

Buck Denver is confused.

Not about his job as a newsman. Buck is confused about Christmas.

He talks about Christmas every year on his news show, but he doesn't understand it. Why do we give presents? Why do we hang stockings?

And what does a guy in a red suit have to do with Jesus' birthday?

Buck Denver is confused.

So his friends come to help him out,
because that's what friends do.

The first to show up are Sunday School Lady and Marcy.
Marcy is confused about Christmas, too.

"At church we have Jesus Christmas,"
she says, "but on TV and at stores...

...we have Santa Christmas.
It's like two different holidays!"

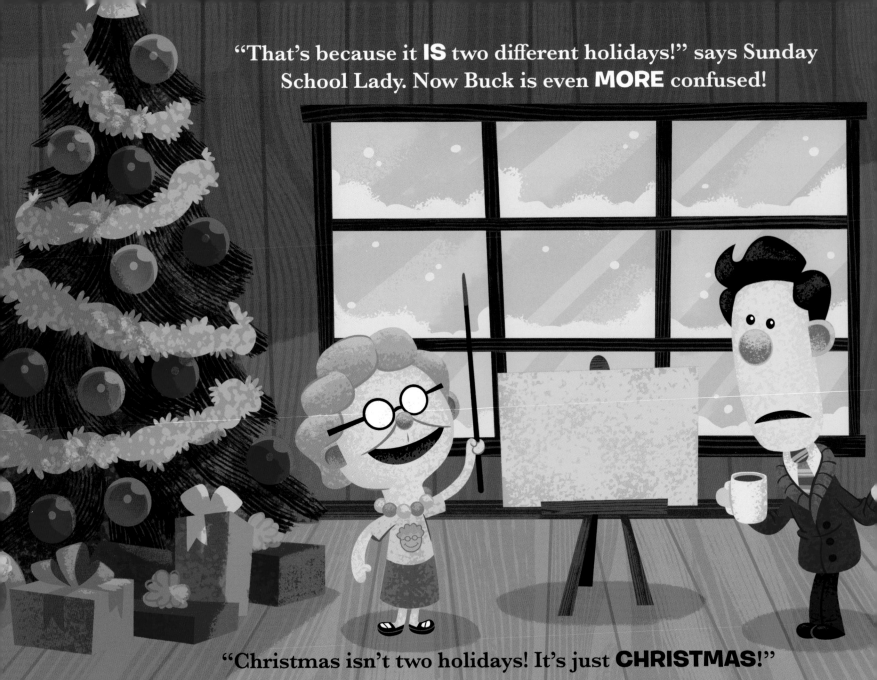

"That's because it **IS** two different holidays!" says Sunday School Lady. Now Buck is even **MORE** confused!

"Christmas isn't two holidays! It's just **CHRISTMAS!**"

"Let me explain with my Magic Flannelgraph," Sunday School Lady says. She never, **NEVER** leaves home without her Magic Flannelgraph.

"For hundreds of years, some churches have had a special service called 'Mass,'" Sunday School Lady explains.

"Once a year, in December, they had a special Mass to celebrate the birth of Jesus, who we also call the 'Christ.' This once-a-year Mass was called the 'Christ's Mass.'"

Buck is **STILL** confused. "What does this have to do with Christmas?"

Sunday School Lady repeats the words louder. **"CHRIST'S MASS."**
Buck still doesn't get it, so Sunday School Lady says it even louder!

"OH!" Buck exclaims. "Christ's Mass—**CHRISTMAS!** That's where the name comes from!"

MASS!

Sunday School Lady gives a big sigh. "This is harder than I thought," she mutters.

"So that's **ONE** of the special days that make up Christmas. What's the other one?" Buck asks.

"Yeah," Marcy chimes in. "And does it involve the guy in the red suit?"

Just then Chuck Waggin and Brother Louie drive up. "Merry Christmas!" they yell. "You mean, Merry **CHRIST'S MASS!**" Marcy yells back.

"Um—sure." Chuck Waggin is confused, too. "If Christmas is all about Jesus, how did Santa Claus become such a big part?"

"Yeah," says Marcy. "Does Santa want us to **FORGET** about Jesus?!?"

Sunday School Lady chuckles. "No! The **REAL** Santa Claus **LOVES** Jesus!"
Buck Denver and his friends look **VERY** confused.

"What's Santa's **REAL** name?" Sunday School Lady asks. No one has any idea. So Sunday School Lady starts reciting a famous poem.

"The stockings were hung by the chimney with care—"

Everyone jumps in—*"In hopes that SAINT NICHOLAS soon would be there!"*

"But who's Saint Nicholas?" they all wonder. "Back to the Magic Flannelgraph!" Sunday School Lady replies.

"Saint Nicholas was a leader in the church a long, long time ago. He loved Jesus very much, and wanted to show Jesus' love to others by helping them."

"His parents had left him a lot of money. So if Nicholas heard that someone needed food or clothes, he would sneak up to their window at night and toss in a bag of coins!"

"Free *money*?" Chuck Waggin hollers.
"That must have made him **VERY** popular!!"
"Yes it did! Soon people all over Europe
had heard about Nicholas and his
nighttime visits!

Especially about the time the bags of coins he tossed to help three poor girls
landed in the stockings they had hung up to dry!"

"Wait—stockings?!?" Brother Louie says. "This sounds familiar!"

"Yep!" Sunday School Lady replies. "So churches gave Nicholas his own special day, called Saint Nicholas Day!

Kids would set out their shoes or their stockings the night before and then wake up early to see what Saint Nicholas had brought them!

They might find a shiny orange, or candy, or a small toy.

Saint Nicholas Day was **VERY** popular with kids!"

Buck Denver is thinking hard. "It sounds like a lot of what we do on Christmas actually comes from Saint Nicholas Day. Is **THAT** the other special day?

"It sure is!" says Sunday School Lady with a smile.

"Saint Nicholas Day was on December 6th each year. The Christ's Mass was on December 25th. About 400 years ago many churches stopped celebrating days dedicated to saints like Saint Nicholas."

"But the traditions of Saint Nicholas Day—like setting out stockings and waiting for a visit from Saint Nick—were **SO** popular, they wouldn't go away! They just moved 19 days later to the day of the Christ's Mass and, together, gave us our **CHRISTMAS!**"

Marcy is amazed. "Wow! So Christmas really **IS** two special days put together!" "And **THAT'S** why it can seem so confusing!" Buck Denver adds.

But Marcy still has one more question. "How did Saint Nicholas's name change to Santa Claus?" Sunday School Lady has an answer for that one, too!

"Stories of Saint Nicholas came to America with Dutch settlers more than 300 years ago. Dutch kids would set out their wooden shoes, waiting for Saint Nicholas to visit. But in Dutch, Saint Nicholas was called Sinterklaas."

"Sinterklaas?!?" the others repeat.
"Yes! Sinterklaas! As other kids heard these stories, Sinterklaas slowly changed to—"
"SANTA CLAUS!"

"Wow! Santa Claus is really Saint Nicholas!" yelled Buck.

"And Christmas today can seem confusing," Marcy continues, "because it's the Christ's Mass **AND** Saint Nicholas Day put **TOGETHER!**"

"That's right!" Sunday School Lady said. "We celebrate Jesus—the greatest gift we could ever get—**AND** we celebrate Saint Nicholas, a man who gave to others because the love of Jesus had been given to him!"

Buck Denver and his friends were glad they learned more about Jesus.
They were glad they learned more about Saint Nicholas.

And they were *especially* glad that Sunday School Lady never, **NEVER** leaves her flannelgraph at home!